MAR 2 6 2014

Bibliothèque publique de la Municipalité de la Nation
Succursale ST ISIDORE Branch
Nation Municipality Public Library

DISCARD / ÉLIMINÉ

D1466174

LA NATION/ST.ISIDORE

IP042108

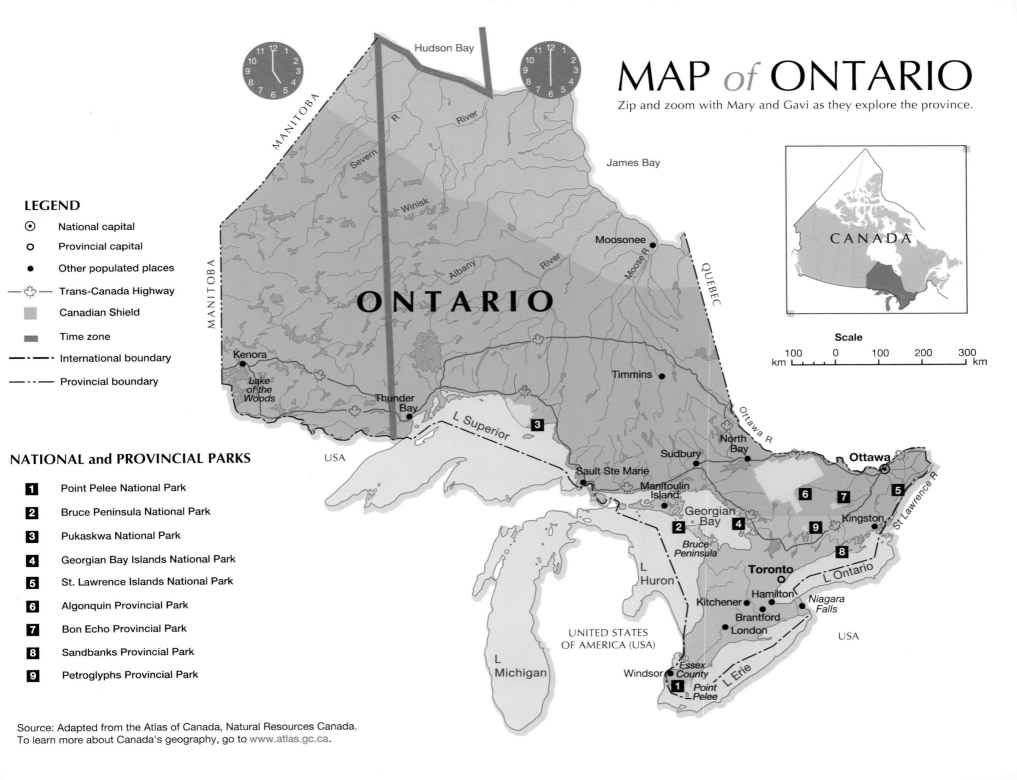

MAP *of* ONTARIO

Zip and zoom with Mary and Gavi as they explore the province.

Hudson Bay

James Bay

MANITOBA

QUEBEC

CANADA

ONTARIO

R

River

Severn

Winisk

Albany

River

Moose R

Moosonee

Kenora

Lake of the Woods

Timmins

Thunder Bay

L Superior

3

USA

Sudbury

North Bay

Ottawa R

Ottawa

St Lawrence R

6

7

5

Kingston

Sault Ste Marie

Manitoulin Island

Georgian Bay

4

9

2

Bruce Peninsula

8

L Huron

Toronto

L Ontario

Kitchener

Hamilton

Niagara Falls

Brantford

London

USA

UNITED STATES OF AMERICA (USA)

L Michigan

Windsor

Essex County

1

Point Pelee

L Erie

LEGEND

⊙ National capital

○ Provincial capital

● Other populated places

🍁 Trans-Canada Highway

⬜ Canadian Shield

⬛ Time zone

–·–·– International boundary

–··–··– Provincial boundary

NATIONAL and PROVINCIAL PARKS

1 Point Pelee National Park

2 Bruce Peninsula National Park

3 Pukaskwa National Park

4 Georgian Bay Islands National Park

5 St. Lawrence Islands National Park

6 Algonquin Provincial Park

7 Bon Echo Provincial Park

8 Sandbanks Provincial Park

9 Petroglyphs Provincial Park

Scale

100 0 100 200 300

km   km

Source: Adapted from the Atlas of Canada, Natural Resources Canada.
To learn more about Canada's geography, go to www.atlas.gc.ca.

For my mother-in-law, Louise Smid, who would have loved reading this story to her grandchildren.
- Gwen Smid

To the first important man in my life, my father, who has always loved loons.
And to June, who helped make this book possible.
- Sonia Nadeau

All rights reserved. No part of this publication may be reproduced, stored in a retrieval system, or transmitted in any form or by any means, without the prior written consent of the publisher or a license from The Canadian Copyright Licensing Agency (Access Copyright). For an Access Copyright license, call toll free to 1-800-893-5777.

Text copyright © 2010 by Gwen Smid
Illustrations copyright © 2010 by Sonia Nadeau

Peanut Butter Press
9-1060 Dakota Street, Winnipeg, MB, R2N 1P2
www.peanutbutterpress.ca

Designed by Christian Love
Edited by Cynthia Guinn Yablonowski

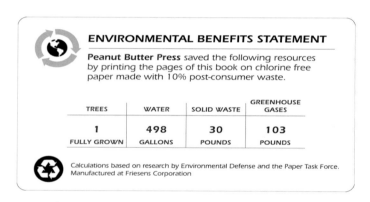

ENVIRONMENTAL BENEFITS STATEMENT

Peanut Butter Press saved the following resources by printing the pages of this book on chlorine free paper made with 10% post-consumer waste.

TREES	WATER	SOLID WASTE	GREENHOUSE GASES
1 FULLY GROWN	498 GALLONS	30 POUNDS	103 POUNDS

Calculations based on research by Environmental Defense and the Paper Task Force. Manufactured at Friesens Corporation

This book was typeset in Optima. The illustrations were rendered in watercolour.

Printed and bound in Canada by Friesens

Library and Archives Canada Cataloguing in Publication

Smid, Gwen, 1979-
    Mary's atlas : Mary meets Ontario / by Gwen Smid ; illustrations by Sonia Nadeau.
ISBN 978-0-9865329-1-7 (bound) — ISBN 978-0-9735579-9-2 (pbk)

    1. Ontario--Juvenile fiction. 2. Ontario--Juvenile literature. I. Nadeau, Sonia, 1974-
II. Title.

PS8637.M53M38 2010   jC813'.6   C2010-900578-3

Mixed Sources
Cert no. SW-COC-001271
© 1996 FSC

Mary's Atlas
Mary Meets Ontario

By Gwen Smid
Illustrations by Sonia Nadeau

Peanut Butter Press

Mary is in trouble.

Her brother just discovered the icky tangle of fake spiders she put in his cereal.
Mary is in her living room frantically searching for her atlas. An ordinary atlas is a collection of maps.

This isn't an ordinary atlas.

When Mary taps the cover three times, she can enter any map. She finds her atlas just in time and – *tap tap tap* – whips it open. The province of Ontario is staring up at her.

The atlas fizzles and sizzles. It splutters and splatters. It bubbles and pops. Mary shrinks smaller and smaller, tinier and tinier, itsy bitsier and itsy bitsier. In a flurry of sparks and mist, Mary vanishes.

The sparks and mist twirl away. Mary is by a lake.

A little loon is wibble wobbling about.

"I'm Gavi. Welcome to Ontario."

"My name's Mary."

Gavi trips on a pinecone. Loons are clumsy critters on land. "This is Algonquin Provincial Park. Let me show you around."

The loon is Ontario's provincial bird, and "gavia" means "loon" in Latin. Look for Gavi on the loonie, Canada's dollar coin.

They zip and zoom over tall white pines on the Canadian Shield.

Flying above the Ottawa River, Mary and Gavi spot a school of floppy trout. The fish, with backpacks and bindle sacks, are swimming in formation of the letters H – E – L – P.

Gavi, a delightful diver, deposits Mary on shore and disappears underwater. He pops up. "The fishvine gossip is that Ontario's Great Lakes are drying up. Those pesky beavers probably built too many dams."

"Let's help," says Mary.

10

Tradition holds that warring Iroquois buried weapons under a white pine, now a symbol of peace.

Ontario holds one-third of the world's fresh water. Only four of the five Great Lakes border the province.

They swish and swoosh along the Ottawa River to Ottawa, Canada's capital city.

On Parliament Hill, the Prime Minister and other elected politicians make important decisions for Canada.

The Peace Tower gargoyles grin grins that only gargoyles can grin.

Atop Parliament Hill flies the Canadian flag, officially adopted on February 15, 1965. The Peace Tower contains the Books of Remembrance of Canada's war dead.

A medley of yummy smells wafts past. "There are lots of eateries in the ByWard Market," explains Gavi. "It's among Canada's biggest and oldest markets."

Mary smiles and consults her atlas. "There's the Rideau Canal. I heard every winter it becomes the largest skating rink in the country!"

They see people strolling and jogging, boating and canoeing along the long canal. It leads Mary and Gavi all the way south to Lake Ontario.

"This Great Lake looks great!" says Gavi.

Mary and Gavi flip and fly around the lake to Toronto, Ontario's capital city. A black squirrel is at the tippy-top of the CN Tower. Gavi bounce-lands. "You have the best view!"

One in four people in Canada live within a few hours of Toronto. The CN Tower is currently the tallest free-standing structure in North America.

"Thanks! I do city tours," says the squirrel. "City Hall, from high in the sky, looks like an eye. The Royal Ontario Museum resembles a glittery crystal. See Casa Loma? It's one of Canada's most beautiful castles, and there's Fort York where Toronto began in 1793."

"Have you heard whether the Great Lakes are drying up?" asks Mary.

The squirrel fluffs his tail and rolls his eyes. "Those pesky beavers probably built too many dams. Check upstream in Lake Erie."

They thank him and wave good-bye.

15

The air grows thick with mist. They hear a splashing noise that turns into a gushing noise that turns into a rumbling noise that turns into a thundering noise.

Niagara Falls spans the international border between Canada and the United States.

Niagara Falls roars and cold water surges.
Mary grips Gavi's neck and shouts, "Watch out!"

Approximately 6 000 cubic metres of water go over the falls every second.

Then, as if a giant tap was turned off, Niagara Falls stops flowing.

Mary frowns. "The lakes upstream must be dry. Hurry!"

They sail and swoop over the drippy falls.

In the sludgy sludge of empty Lake Erie, some fish are playing *Go Fish*, while others are making mud pies to pass the time.

"Lake Erie is really empty," says Gavi. "Good thing there are puddles so the fish can be comfy."

During the War of 1812, Laura Secord warned the governing British in Canada of an attack on the Niagara Peninsula, the area between Lake Ontario and Lake Erie.

Mary checks her atlas. "There's Point Pelee! We're as far south as we can get in Canada."

"If we keep travelling straight west, we'll reach northern California." Gavi is one brainy bird.

A blue jay tweedles, "Tool-ool! Tool-ool!"

A marsh wren twitters, "Chet! Chet! Chet! Chet!"

A robin tweets, "Tut! Tut! Tut! Tut!"

A cardinal squawks as Gavi collides into the choir. He picks himself up and bursts into song. Loons may be ungainly on land, but they sure can sing!

Mary applauds after Gavi's enchanting solo.

20   *Point Pelee is the best inland spot in North America to see hundreds of species of birds returning in spring.*

Bowing, Gavi says, "I'd love to keep singing, but we're trying to find out why the Great Lakes are dry."

The conductor, a skink, rolls his eyes. "Those pesky beavers probably built too many dams. Check upstream in Lake Huron. Focus, birdies! A-one, a-two, a-one-two-three!"

They thank him and wave good-bye.

Further north, in the mucky muck of empty Lake Huron, some fish are playing *Fish and Ladders*, while others are applying mud masks to pass the time.

"Lake Huron is really, really empty," says Mary.

The five-lined skink is Ontario's only indigenous lizard.

To the east, they see spectacular Bruce Peninsula with gnarled, twisted trees growing out of the lofty cliffs.

"Some of these trees are a thousand years old." Gavi bumps along the ground.

Mary steps closer to the cliff, admiring the orchids and trilliums.

Suddenly, with a creak and a crumble, the ground collapses under Mary, and she skitters downhill.

"Help!" she hollers, grasping at roots.

A long twiggy hand scoops her up. The ancient tree twists into a smile, returning Mary to safety.

"Are you okay?" Gavi picks a leaf out of her hair.

Mary nods in relief.

They dipsy-doodle around Georgian Bay, over Manitoulin Island, and into Lake Superior.

The Niagara Escarpment, a long, steep cliff system with stunning waterfalls, runs from Manitoulin Island, along the Bruce Peninsula, all the way to Niagara Falls.

The Group of Seven created many famous paintings near this region.

In the gunky goo of empty Lake Superior, some fish are playing *Fishopoly*, while others are mud wrestling to pass the time.

"Lake Superior is really, really, really empty," says Mary. "It has the highest elevation of all the Great Lakes, so the problem must've started here."

Gavi crashes into a large rock.

"A rock shouldn't be wiggly," says Mary as the ground starts to wiggle.

"A rock shouldn't be quivery," says Gavi as the ground starts to quiver.

"And you shouldn't be standing on my nose. Ah-choo!" the rock sneezes.

Mary and Gavi are flung into the air. From above, the two friends see that the rock looks like a giant lying on his back.

"The Sleeping Giant!" gasps Gavi.

Aboriginal legends surround the mysterious Sleeping Giant, a natural landform that can be seen from Thunder Bay.

"What happened to my lake?" Giant asks.

Gavi rolls his eyes. "Probably those pesky beavers."

"Golly." Giant grimaces. "I must have kicked out the lake's plug while swimming last night. I'm not allowed to move during the day. I scare kids."

"I'm not scared," says Mary.

"Boo!" quips Giant.

Mary and Gavi fly over Lake Superior's sludgy, mucky, gooey bottom looking for the plug.

"There it is!" Mary exclaims. They struggle and strain to move it.

Suddenly, a merry ruckus erupts from a bevy of beavers.

"Hello! Can you help?" calls Mary.

Together, they struggle and strain, strain and struggle, then *THWUMP*! The plug plops into place.

"How do we fill the lakes?" wonders Gavi.

Picking wood from her teeth, an old beaver smiles. "We know a secret."

The beaver is a national symbol due to its role in the fur trade.

The beavers start drumming with their flat tails.
Ta-dum, ta-dum, ta-dah-ta-dah, ta-dum.
Clouds twist together. The beavers drum, the clouds unfurl and *BOOM! CRACK! WHOOSH!* Rain pours down. Lake Superior overflows, spilling into Lake Huron, then Lake Erie, over Niagara Falls to Lake Ontario, and finally down the mighty St. Lawrence Seaway into the Atlantic Ocean.

"I've been blaming you all this time for the really, really, really, really empty lakes," says Gavi to the beavers. "We couldn't have done it without you!"

They shake, wing to paw.

The 1000 Islands are a world famous vacation spot on the St. Lawrence River.

Gavi turns to Mary. "I have friends just west of here in Lake of the Woods. It's beautiful country, and we'll get to cross a time zone. It's like going back in time an hour."

Mary hugs Gavi. "I'd better go home. Thanks for the adventure!"

"Come visit again," says Gavi.

Mary taps her atlas – *tap tap tap* – and opens it to the page where she lives.

The atlas fizzles and sizzles. It splutters and splatters. It bubbles and pops. Mary grows bigger and bigger, taller and taller, larger and larger. In a flurry of sparks and mist, she is back in her living room.

Mary hears her brother in the hallway.
"I guess I'd better go apologize," she mutters.
She spots her tub of sneezing powder. "Now that would be interesting."

Then Mary smiles.

Dear Readers,

There are many interesting places in Ontario that we did not get a chance to visit. Here are just a few:

Lake of the Woods
Explore more than 105 000 kilometres of shoreline while canoeing, fishing, or camping.

Thunder Bay
East of Thunder Bay is the Terry Fox Memorial, located where this Canadian hero had to end his Marathon of Hope in support of cancer research.

Kingston
Sir John A. Macdonald went to school, practised law, and was buried in Kingston. He became Canada's first Prime Minister at Confederation on July 1, 1867.

Moosonee
Experience the beauty of the North! Moosonee is only accessible via air or the Polar Bear Express train.

Brantford
Visit the birthplace of hockey legend Wayne Gretzky.

Essex County
This was the safe haven of the "Underground Railroad" for escaping slaves.

The National and Provincial Parks
Ontario's five national parks include Point Pelee National Park.

There are more than 320 provincial parks.

In Petroglyphs Provincial Park, you will find Kinoomaagewaapkong, Canada's biggest grouping of Aboriginal rock carvings.

Are you interested in seeing over 260 rock paintings? Then visit Bon Echo Provincial Park for one of North America's premiere collections.

If you love beaches, consider Sandbanks Provincial Park, the world's largest freshwater baymouth sand dunes.

We hope you have fun meeting Ontario!

Your friends,

Mary & Gavi